It's Easy To Play
Robbie Williams

Wise Publications
part of The Music Sales Group

London / New York / Paris / Sydney / Copenhagen / Berlin / Madrid / Tokyo

Published by
Wise Publications
14-15 Berners Street, London W1T 3LJ, UK.

Exclusive Distributors:
Music Sales Limited
Distribution Centre, Newmarket Road, Bury St Edmunds, Suffolk IP33 3YB, UK.
Music Sales Pty Limited
120 Rothschild Avenue, Rosebery, NSW 2018, Australia.

Order No. AM988130
ISBN 1-84609-814-9
This book © Copyright 2006 by Wise Publications.

Edited by Jessica Williams.
Arranged and engraved by Camden Music.
Cover photograph courtesy of London Features International.
Printed in the the EU.

Your Guarantee of Quality
As publishers, we strive to produce every book to the highest commercial standards.
The music has been freshly engraved and the book has been carefully designed to
minimise awkward page turns and to make playing from it a real pleasure.
Particular care has been given to specifying acid-free, neutral-sized paper made from
pulps which have not been elemental chlorine bleached.
This pulp is from farmed sustainable forests and was produced with special regard for the environment.
Throughout, the printing and binding have been planned to ensure a sturdy,
attractive publication which should give years of enjoyment.
If your copy fails to meet our high standards, please inform us and we will gladly replace it.

www.musicsales.com

Angels

Words & Music by Robbie Williams & Guy Chambers

me, I know that life won't break me, when I come to call,

she won't for-sake me.

I'm lov-ing an-gels in-stead.

2. When I'm feel-ing weak and my pain

walks down a one-way street, I look a-bove,

and I know I'll al-ways be blessed with love,

and   as the feel-ing grows,   she brings   flesh to my bones   and

D.S. al Coda

when love is dead,   I'm lov-ing an-gels in-stead.__   And through it   all,__

⊕ **Coda**

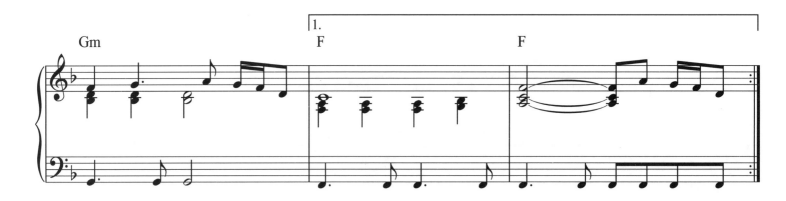

9

Advertising Space

Words & Music by Robbie Williams & Stephen Duffy

1. There's no earth-ly way of know-ing what was in your heart when
2. Through your eyes the world was burn-ing. "Please be gen-tle, I'm

it stopped go - ing. The whole world shook, a storm was blow - ing through___ you.
___ still learn - ing", you seemed to say,___ as you kept turn - ing up.___

Wait - ing for___ God to stop___ this and up to your___ neck
They pois - oned you___ with com - pro - mise, at what point did___ you re -

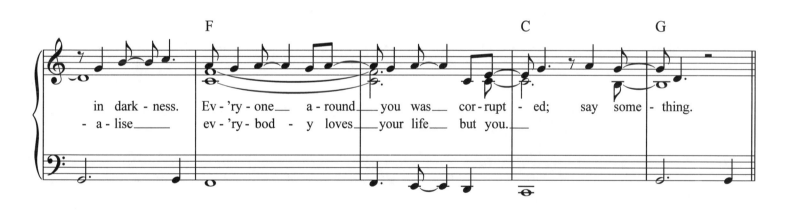

in dark - ness. Ev - 'ry - one___ a - round___ you was___ cor - rupt - ed; say some - thing.
- a - lise___ ev - 'ry - bod - y loves___ your life___ but you.___

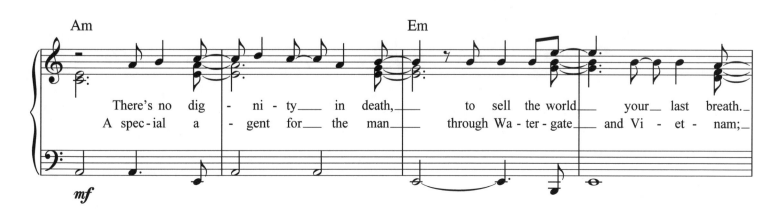

There's no dig - ni - ty___ in death,___ to sell the world___ your___ last breath.___
A spec - ial a - gent for___ the man___ through Wa - ter - gate___ and Vi - et - nam;___

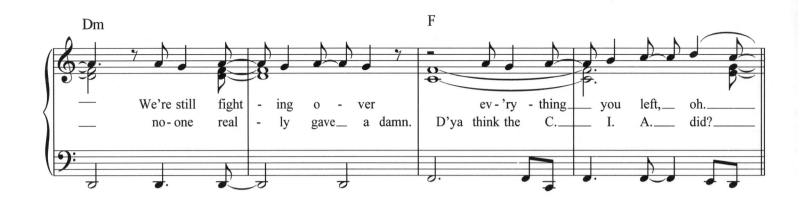

Dm ... F

We're still fight - ing o - ver ev - 'ry - thing _ you left, _ oh. _
no - one real - ly gave _ a damn. D'ya think the C. I. A. _ did? _

%. C ... Em

I saw you stand - ing at _ the gates _ when Mar - lon Bran - do passed _ a - way. _
On %: No - one learned _ from your _ mis takes, _ we let our pro - phets go _ to waste. _

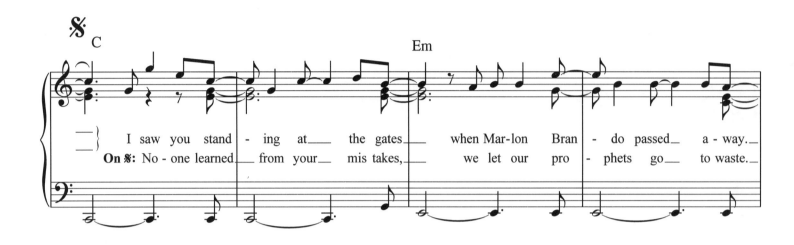

Am ... G ... F

You had that look _ up - on _ your face, _ ad - ver - tis - ing space, _ yeah. _
All that's left, _ in a - ny case, _ is ad - ver - tis - ing space, _ oh. _

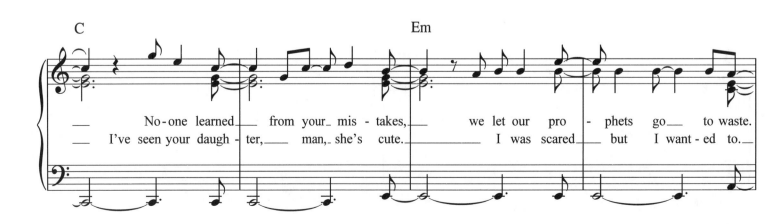

C ... Em

No - one learned _ from your _ mis - takes, _ we let our pro - phets go _ to waste.
I've seen your daugh - ter, _ man, she's cute. _ I was scared _ but I want - ed to.

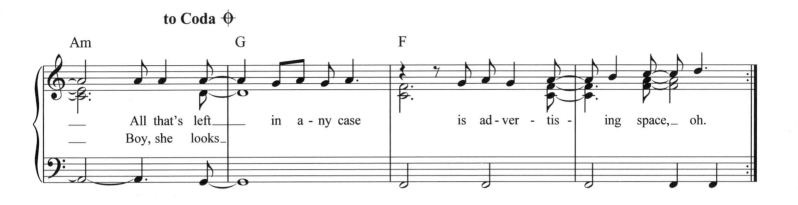

All that's left___ in a - ny case is ad - ver - tis - ing space,_ oh.
Boy, she looks___

mp

Oh.___

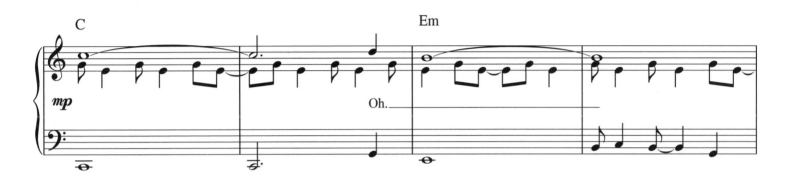

Ah.___

Ooh.___

D.S. al Coda   ⊕ **Coda**

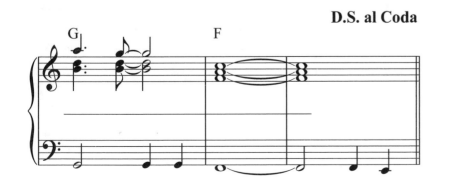

___ a lot___ like you.

Feel

Words & Music By Robbie Williams & Guy Chambers

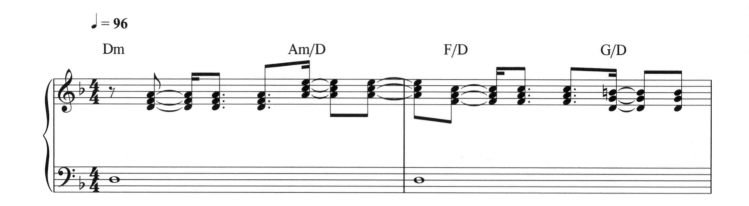

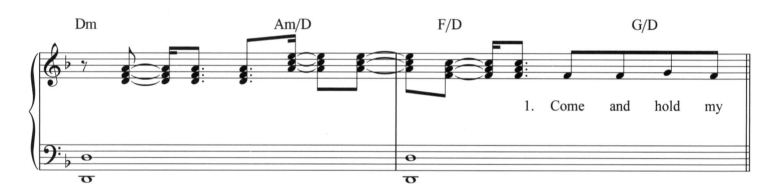

1. Come and hold my

hand,
(2.) die,

I wan-na con-tact__ the liv - ing.
but I ain't keen on liv-ing ei - ther.

Not sure I un-der- stand____ this role I've been giv -
Be - fore I fall in love____ I'm pre - par - ing to leave__

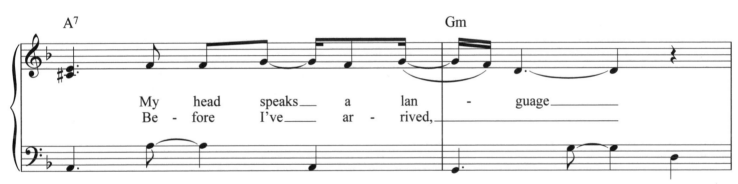

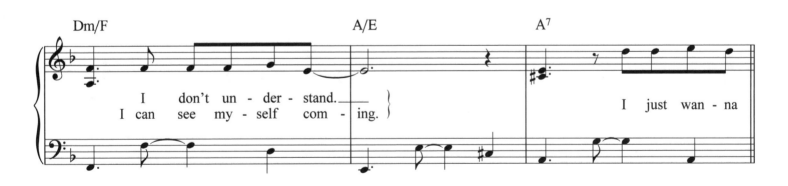

16

I just wan-na feel real love___ and a life ev-er af-

-ter.___ There's a hole in my soul, you can see it in my face,

it's a real big place.___

Come and hold my hand,___ I wan-na con-tact_ the

Let Me Entertain You

Words & Music by Robbie Williams & Guy Chambers

Funky Rock ♩ = 124

1. Hell is gone and Heav-en's here, there's noth-ing left for you to fear;
2. Life's too short for you to die so grab your-self an a-li-bi.

shake your ass, come o-ver here, now scream. I'm a burn-ing ef-fi-gy of
Heav-en knows, your moth-er lied, mon cher. Se-par-ate your right from wrongs,

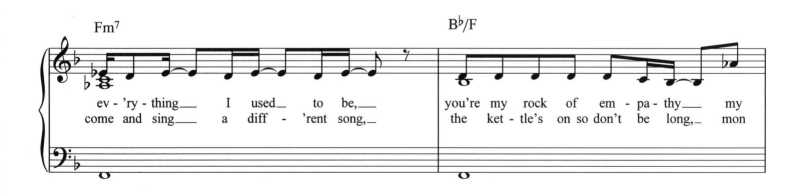

ev-'ry-thing I used to be, you're my rock of em-pa-thy my
come and sing a diff-'rent song, the ket-tle's on so don't be long, mon

popped a pill___ and fell___ a-sleep,___ the dew is wet but the grass is sweet,___ my

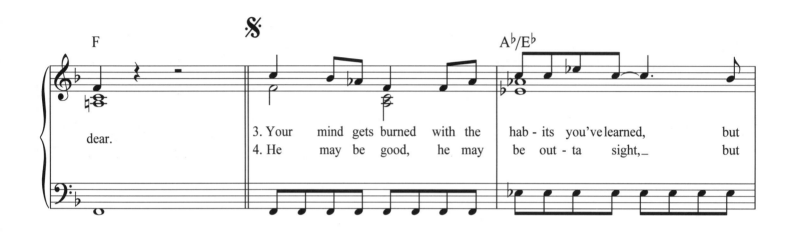

dear.

3. Your mind gets burned with the hab-its you've learned, but
4. He may be good, he may be out-ta sight,___ but

we're the ge-ner-a - tion that's got-ta be heard.___ You're tired of your teach-ers and your
he can't be here, so come a - round___ to-night.___ Here is the place___ where the

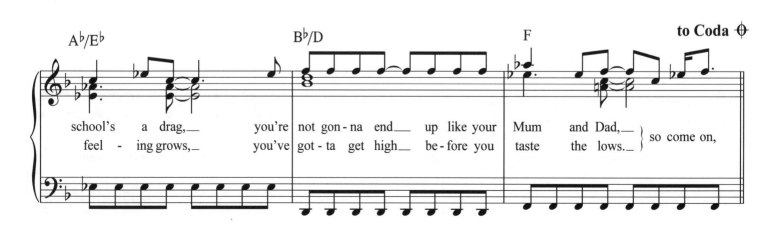

school's a drag,___ you're not gon-na end___ up like your Mum and Dad,___ } so come on,
feel - ing grows,___ you've got-ta get high___ be-fore you taste the lows.___ }

D.S. al Coda

Coda

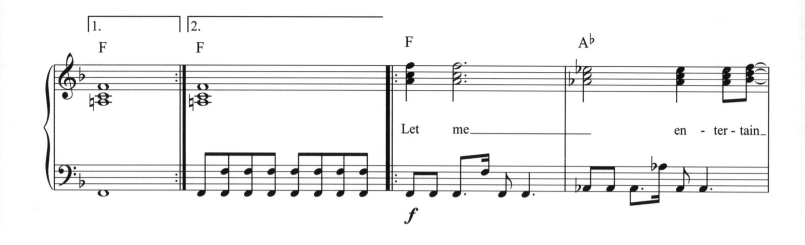

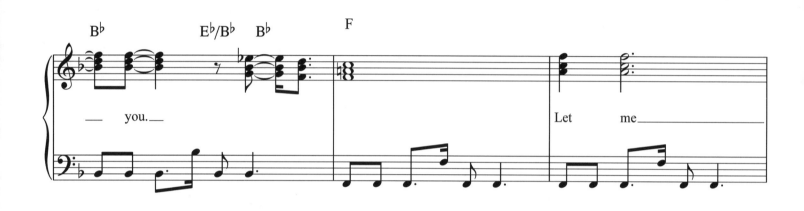

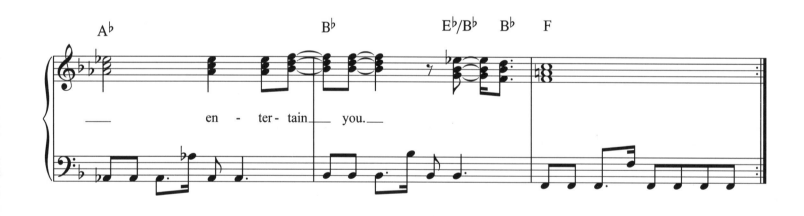

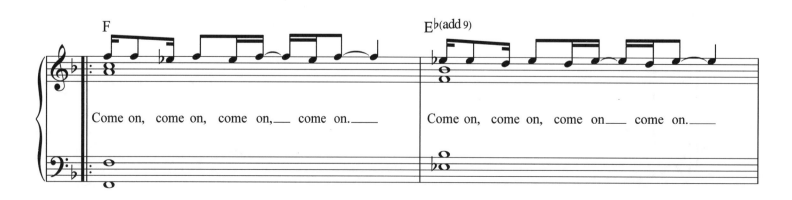

Misunderstood

Words & Music by Robbie Williams & Stephen Duffy

Steadily, with expression ♩ = 60

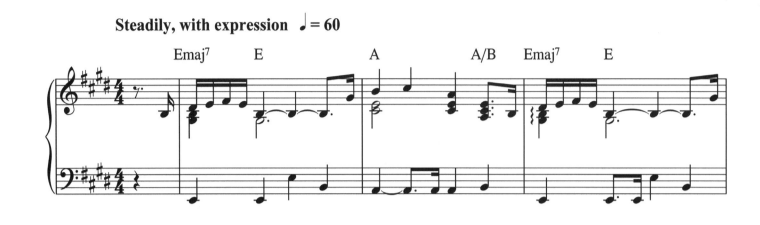

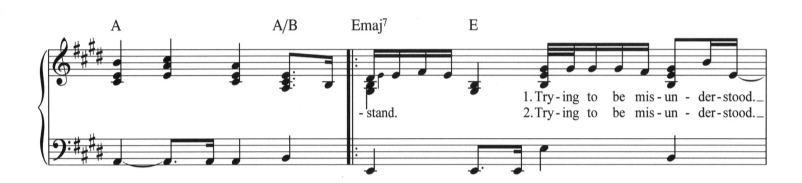

1. Try-ing to be mis-un-der-stood.
2. Try-ing to be mis-un-der-stood.

But it does-n't do me a-ny good.
Just a pro-duct of my child-hood.

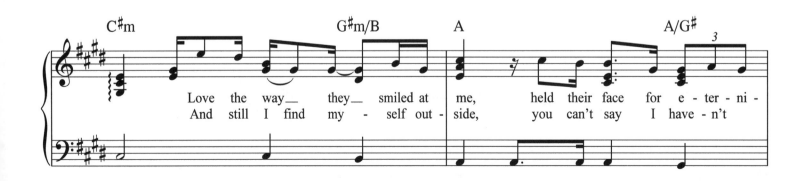

Love the way they smiled at me, held their face for e-ter-ni-
And still I find my-self out-side, you can't say I have-n't

None of this___ was planned.___ Take me by___ the hand,___

just don't try___ and un-der- | just don't try___ and un-der-

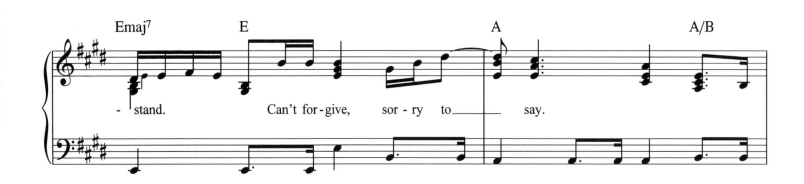

-stand. Can't for-give, sor-ry to___ say.

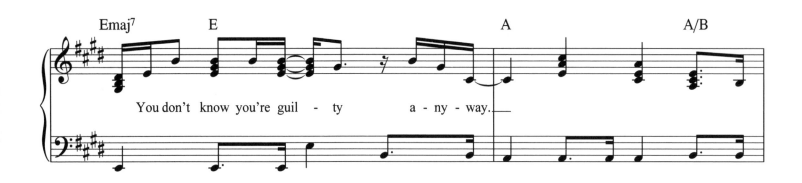

You don't know you're guil - ty a-ny-way.___

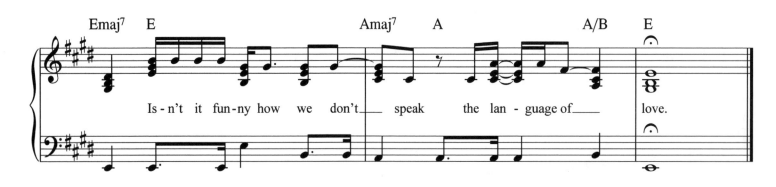

Is-n't it fun-ny how we don't___ speak the lan - guage of___ love.

No Regrets

Words & Music by Robbie Williams & Guy Chambers

Steadily, with expression ♩ = 104

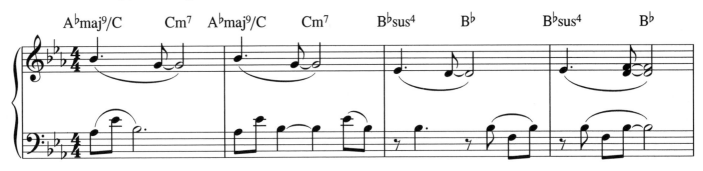

1. Tell me a sto - ry   where we all change

and we'd live our lives   to - ge - ther   and not es - tranged.

I did-n't lose my mind, it was mine to give a-way.

Could-n't stay to watch me cry, you did-n't have the time, so I soft-ly slip a-way.

No re-grets, they don't work.

No re-grets now, they on-ly hurt.

Sing me a love song,
I know they're still talk - ing,

- ing wrong___ when you did-n't like my mo - ther. I don't want___

___ to hate,___ but that's all you've left___ me with. A bit- ter af -

D.S. al Coda

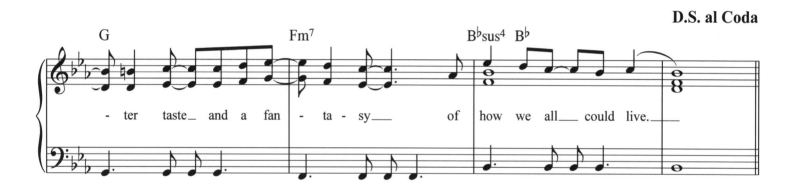

- ter taste___ and a fan - ta - sy___ of how we all___ could live.___

𝄋 **Coda**

_____ Re-mem-ber the pho - to - graphs___ (in - sane), The ones where we___

___ all laughed (how lame). We were ha-ving the time___ of our lives,___ well thank___

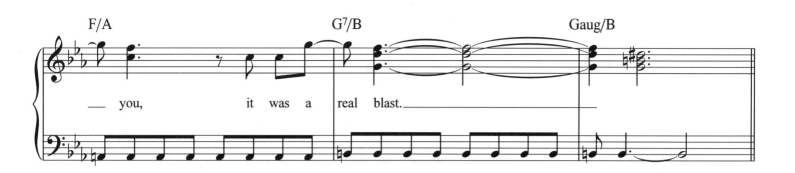

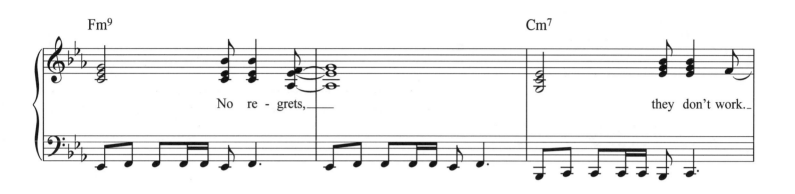

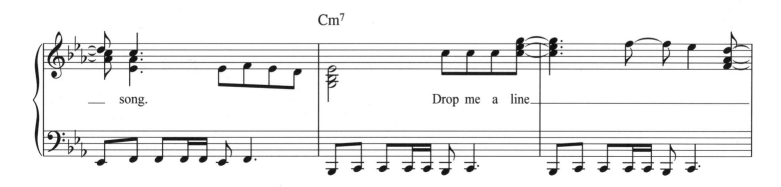

I just wanted to stay. Every time you looked at me and every time you smiled, I felt so vacant;

you treated me like a child. I loved the way we used to laugh, I loved the way we used to smile.

Often I sit down and think of you for a while. And then it passes me by and I

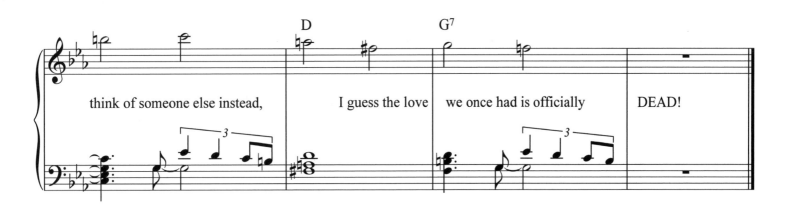

think of someone else instead, I guess the love we once had is officially DEAD!

Rock DJ

Words & Music by Robbie Williams, Guy Chambers,
Kelvin Andrews, Nelson Pigford & Ekundayo Paris

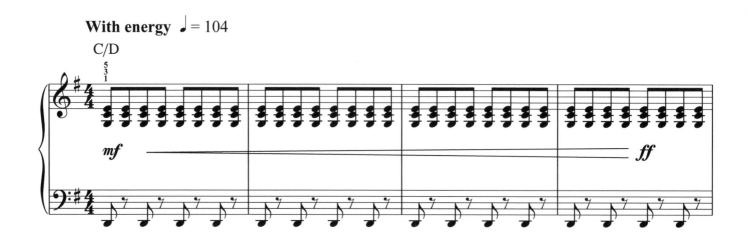

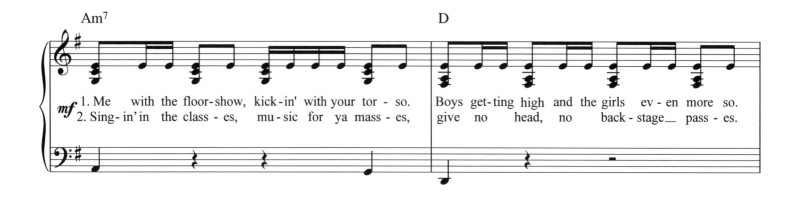

1. Me with the floor-show, kick-in' with your tor - so. Boys get-ting high and the girls ev - en more so.
2. Sing-in' in the class - es, mu - sic for ya mass - es, give no head, no back-stage pass - es.

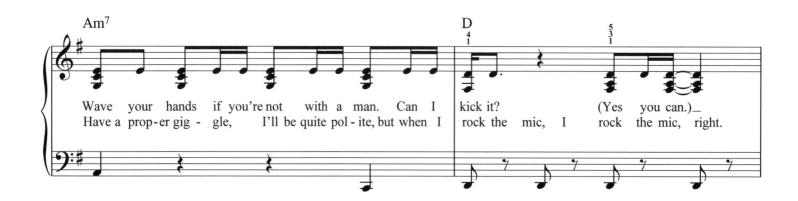

Wave your hands if you're not with a man. Can I kick it? (Yes you can.)
Have a prop-er gig - gle, I'll be quite pol - ite, but when I rock the mic, I rock the mic, right.

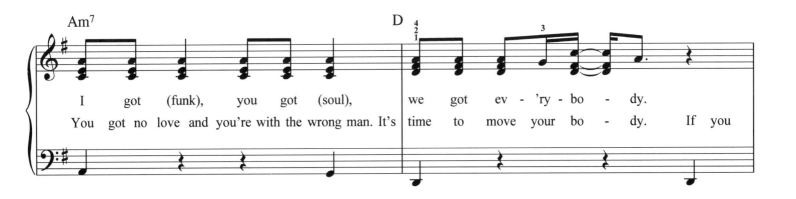

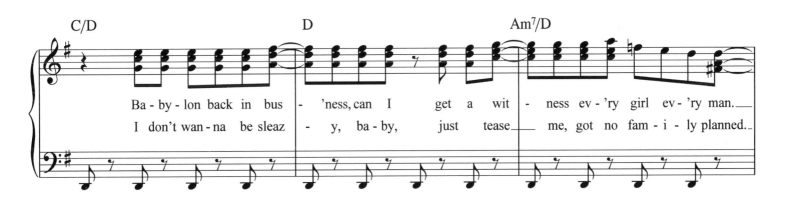

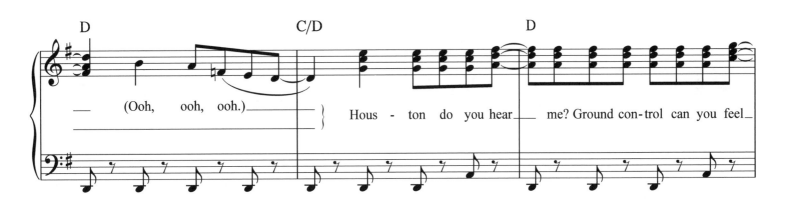

38

Rudebox

Words & Music by Robbie Shakespeare, Kelvin Andrews,
William Collins, Bill Laswell, Robbie Williams, Daniel Mould & Edmund Aiken

Electro rap ♩ = 100

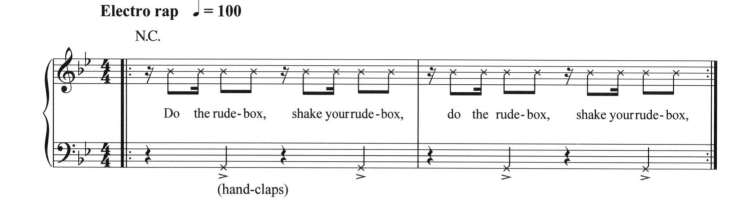

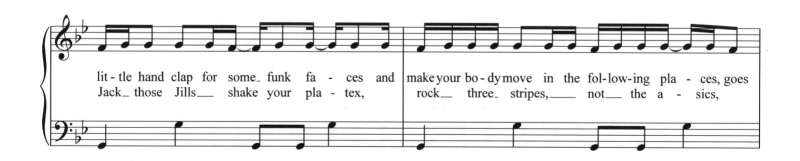

up your back and then down your spine___ and when it | hits your head…
A. D. I. D. A. S. | Old school 'cause it's the best, (yes!)

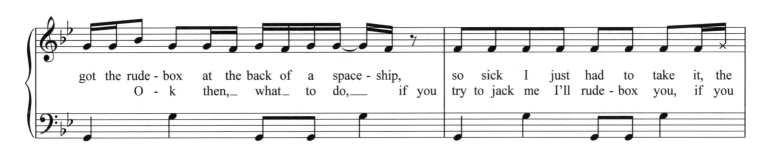

O - k then back to bass - heads, dance___ like you just won at the spe-cial O - lym - pics, I
T. K. Max cost less,_____ (yes!)_____ | Jack - son looks a mess_____ (bless).

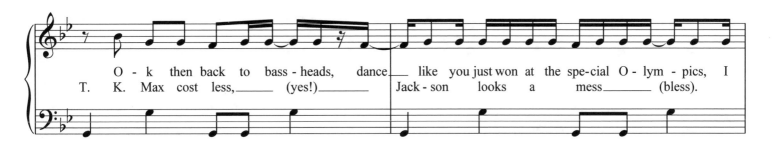

got the rude - box at the back of a space - ship, | so sick I just had to take it, the
O - k then,_ what_ to do,___ if you | try to jack me I'll rude - box you, if you

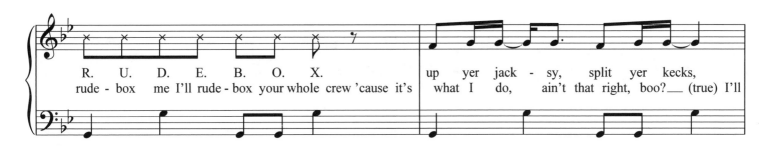

R. U. D. E. B. O. X. | up yer jack - sy, split yer kecks,
rude - box me I'll rude - box your whole crew 'cause it's | what I do, ain't that right, boo?__ (true) I'll

sing a song of sem - tex, (sem - tex) poc - ket full of | du - rex, (dur - ex) bo - dy full of man - drex.
ride with you if you can get me to the bor - der 'cause the | sher - iff's af - ter me for what I did to his daugh - ter, I

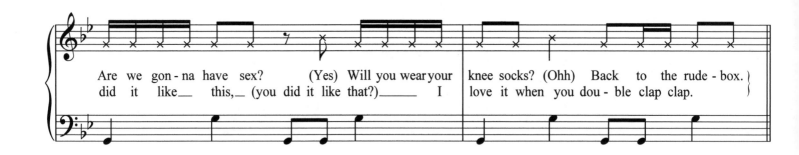

Are we gon - na have sex? (Yes) Will you wear your knee socks? (Ohh) Back to the rude - box.
did it like this, (you did it like that?) I love it when you dou - ble clap clap.

Gm Am B♭ Gm

Got this dou - ble fan - ta - sy where we just ne - ver stop, I've

Gm Am B♭maj⁷

got one des - ign and that's to funk you to the top.

Gm Am B♭ Gm

Know what's on my mind, there's on - ly one thing you will find, I

Gm Am B♭maj⁷

got one de - sign and that's to bump un - til you drop.

Verse 3

Ok then, check the tan line, make your body shape like you've stood on a landmine,

Call me on my mobile not the landline, and the jack the mainline at the same time.

Ok, this is what we do, got a jam so fresh it's nice for you.

Ok, give it what you got and dial 8-0-8 for the bass to drop.

Ok then, what's the fracas, grab your cardy, your lead hat and the bus pass,

You don't sweat much for a fat lass, grab your rudebox 'cause your box is righteous.

Ok bum, rush the show, I got high speed dubbing on my stereo,

And all the tunes in the box are the cherrio, I know I told you before, did you hear me though?

She's The One

Words & Music by Karl Wallinger

Verse 3:
Though the sea will be strong,
I know we'll carry on.
'Cause if there's somebody calling me on, she's the one.
If there's somebody calling me on, she's the one.

Verse 4:
I was her, she was me,
We were one, we were free.
And if there's somebody calling me on, she's the one.
If there's somebody calling me on, she's the one...*etc*.

Radio

Words & Music by Robbie Williams & Stephen Duffy

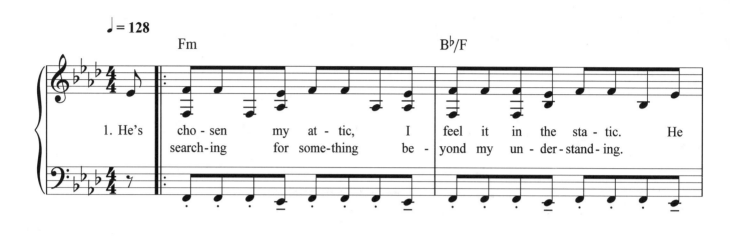

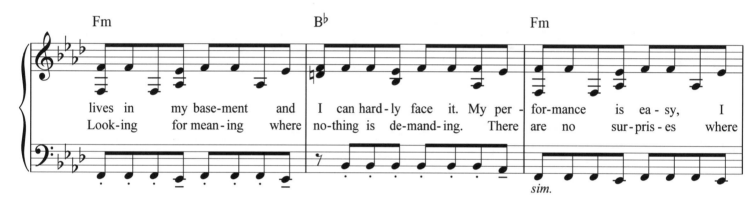

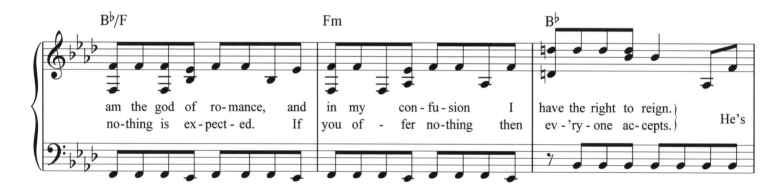

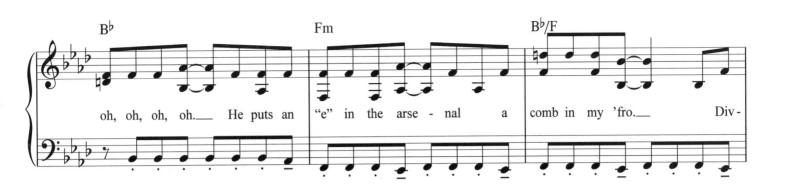

oh, oh, oh, oh.___ He puts an "e" in the arse - nal a comb in my 'fro.___ Div-

-ine re - tri - bu - tion and a - way we'll go.___ Some - thing's hap - pen - ing,

I can feel___ it, mov - ing out___ of time___ you'll hear___ it.

Fall - ing in___ the way___ you fear___ it. Jump - ing, thump - ing,

shout out some - thing. Jump - ing, thump - ing, shout out some - thing.

Lis - ten to the ra - di - o____ and you will hear the songs__ __ you know.__ Make it ef - fer - ves - cent here__ and you might have a job__ my dear.__ My dear.__

2. I'm

Ouch!

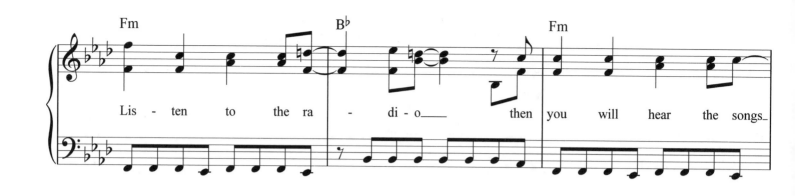

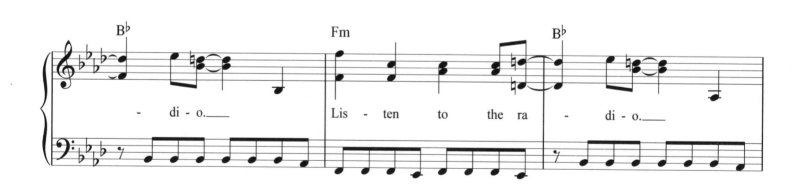

Somethin' Stupid

Words & Music by C. Carson Parks

Strong

Words & Music by Robbie Williams & Guy Chambers

D.S. al Coda

⊕ **Coda**

Repeat 4 times and fade

And you know___ and you know___ 'cause my life's a___ mess,_____

and I'm try - ing to grow.___ Ah,_____ hey,___ hey.

Life's too short to be___ a - fraid,___

take a pill to numb the pain,___ you don't have to take the blame._____

Supreme

Words & Music by Robbie Williams, Dino Fekaris,
Frederick Perren, Guy Chambers & Francois de Roubaix

With a 'Gloria Gaynor drive'! ♩ = 96

1.Oh,   it seemed for -
(Verse 2 see block lyric)

- ev - er stopped to - day,___ all the lone - ly hearts___ in Lon - don caught a plane___
sim.

___ and flew a - way.___ And all the best___ wo - men___ are mar - ried,___ all the hand-

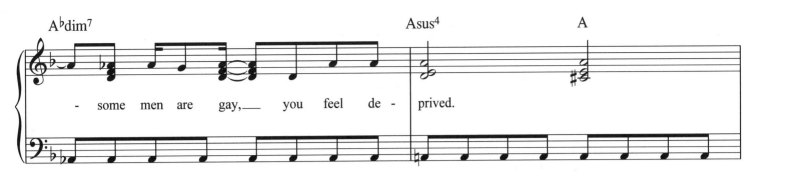

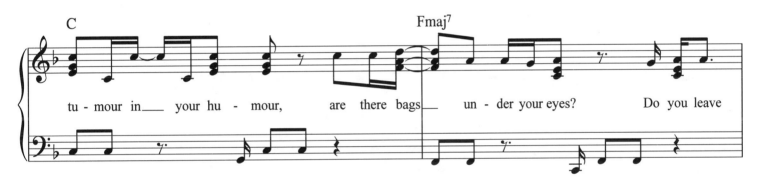

D.S. al Coda   ⊕ **Coda**

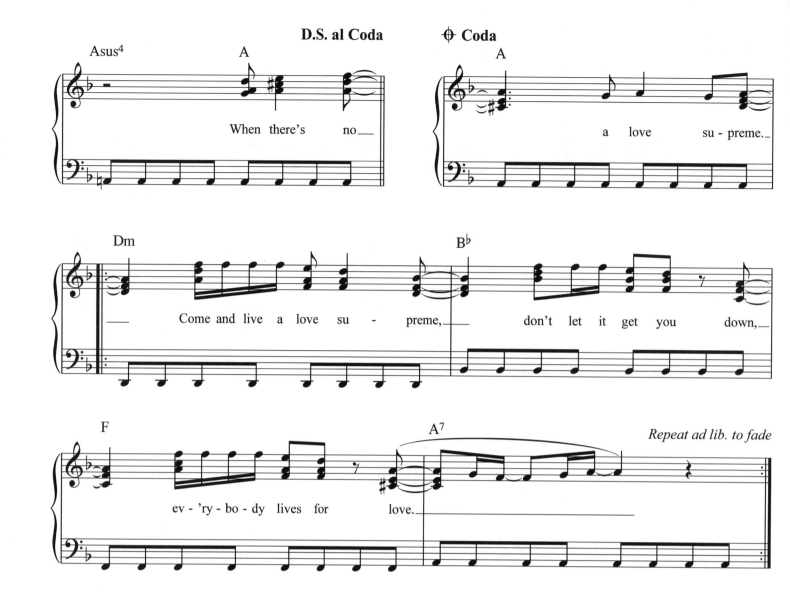

When there's no___

a love su-preme.___

Come and live a love su - preme,___ don't let it get you down,___

ev - 'ry - bo - dy lives for love.___

Repeat ad lib. to fade

Verse 2:

Oh, what are you really looking for?

Another partner in your life to abuse and to adore?

Is it lovey dovey stuff,

Do you need a bit of rough?

Get on your knees,

Yeah, turn down the love songs that you hear,

'Cause you can't avoid the sentiment

That echoes in your ear.

Saying love will stop the pain,

Saying love will kill the fear.

Do you believe?

You must believe...

When there's no love in town *etc.*

123456789